Heads I win! Tottenham's Paul Stewart climbs above Kent Neilsen, Aston Villa's Danish international defender, during an exciting tussle at White Hart Lane.

D0184597

3

6

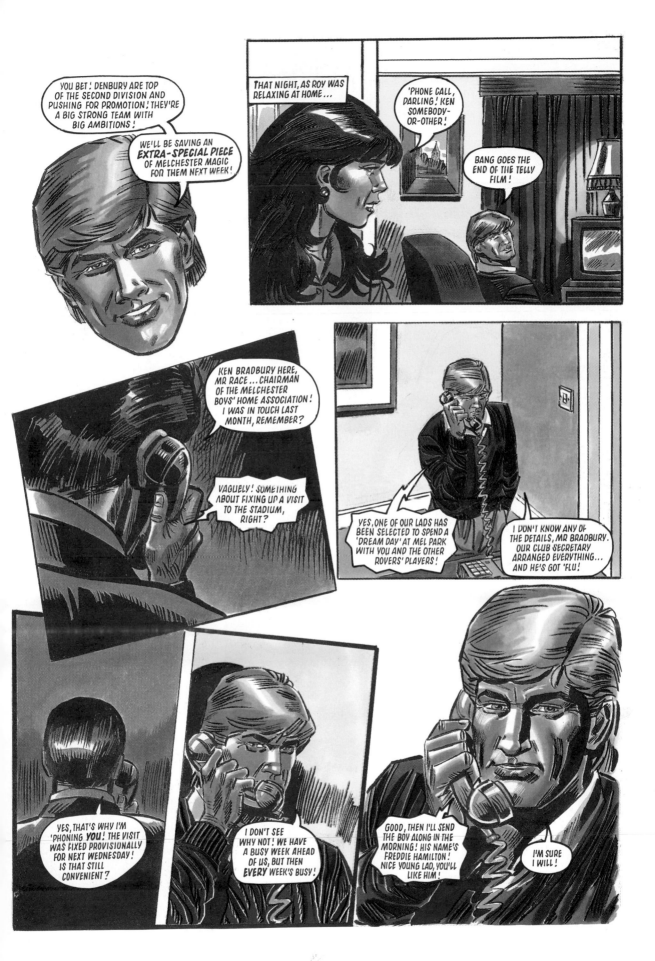

8

BANG GOES OUR GAME PLAN! UNITED HAVE GRABBED THAT EARLY GOAL INSTEAD OF US!

AND THEY MADE US LOOK LIKE A LOAD OF TAILORS' DUMMIES! LET'S PULL OUR SOCKS UP!

BUT EVERY ATTACKING MOVE THAT ROVERS MADE WAS STOPPED DEAD! AND AT HALF-TIME...

STILL ONE-NIL DOWN! EVERYTHING WE DO IS GOING WRONG, ROY, WHAT'S THE—?

HOLD IT! UP THERE IN THE DIRECTORS' BOX...

...THAT'S THE 'DREAM DAY' KID, FREDDIE HAMILTON! WHO'S HE SITTING NEXT TO?

ONE OF THE DENBURY UNITED DIRECTORS! A BOOKMAKER...FLASH HARRY HAMILTON, HE'S CALLED! YOU DON'T THINK..?

OH, YES, I DO! SUDDENLY EVERYTHING IS CRYSTAL CLEAR! DO ME A FAVOUR, MERV...

...CHECK IN THE CLUB SECRETARY'S DIARY AS TO WHEN WE'D FIXED THAT 'DREAM DAY' DATE WITH THE MELCHESTER BOYS' HOME ASSOCIATION!

TRAINER MERVYN WALLACE WAS BACK WITHIN MINUTES!

THE VISIT IS BOOKED FOR THE TWENTY-FOURTH... TWO WEEKS FROM NOW! FOR A BOY CALLED IAN PARKER!

I'VE ALSO DISCOVERED THAT FLASH HARRY HAMILTON HAS A SON! HIS NAME IS FREDDIE!

I THOUGHT AS MUCH! FLASH HARRY FINDS OUT WE'VE GOT A 'DREAM DAY' DATE LINED UP, AND 'PHONES ME PRETENDING TO BE KEN BRADBURY!

YOU MEAN TO PLANT HIS OWN SON IN MEL PARK FOR THE DAY AS A SPY?

YES! SHY, POLITE, BLUE-EYED FREDDIE HAMILTON KNOCKED THAT BRUSH OVER AS HE LISTENED TO OUR TACTICAL TALK LAST WEDNESDAY!

TELL THE LADS TO GATHER ROUND, MERV...THIS IS WHAT WE'RE GOING TO DO...

11

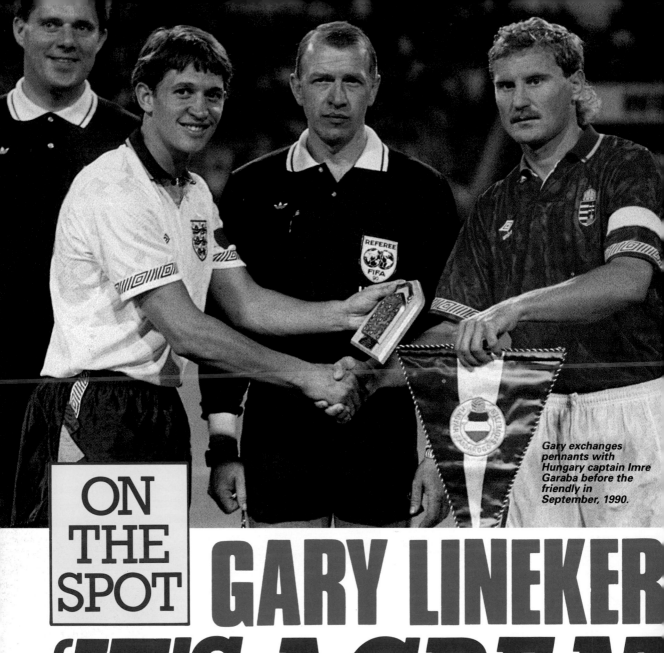

Gary exchanges pennants with Hungary captain Imre Garaba before the friendly in September, 1990.

GARY LINEKER

'IT'S A GREAT

... says our star writer as he tells us all about being the man-in-the-armband for England.

IT WAS A GREAT THRILL and the fulfilment of a long-standing personal ambition when Graham Taylor appointed me as England's skipper, back in September 1990.

There is no greater honour a player can enjoy than captaining his country.

And speaking as a red-blooded Englishman there is no better feeling than leading the team out of the tunnel and on to Wembley's lush green turf.

Nevertheless it still

came as something of a surprise when the Boss first told me that I would succeed Bryan Robson as Captain of England.

Until then I'd only ever skippered a top level side on one occasion.

That was Spurs – against Wimbledon at Plough Lane the previous season. Our regular captain Gary Mabbutt and his deputy Terry Fenwick were both injured, so Terry Venables handed me the armband.

We lost 0–1 that day and I didn't really expect to be a captain again. It was strictly a one-off.

But Graham Taylor obviously had other ideas!

Of course, Bryan Robson was a marvellous role model for any England captain and I had made most of my international appearances under his leadership. He's a tremendous player who was a fine example to everyone in the team.

OB!'

He was most definitely a hard act to follow.

I've really enjoyed my term in the job so far. With all the extra responsibility it's certainly been an interesting challenge.

The main differences between being a regular member of the squad and being the captain have been *off* the field. For instance, I now have

CONTINUED OVERLEAF

GARY LINEKER

CONTINUED

a much closer contact with the Boss than I had with Bobby Robson. Graham Taylor consults me about team policy and asks my opinions on a number of topics.

And of course, as skipper I'm the link man between the manager and the team. It's up to me to relay certain instructions to the other players and so on.

I'm also the chief link between the players and the media, a role I enjoy – up to a point!

Being captain *on* the field hasn't made much of a noticeable difference to me. I've always been a talker and a shouter anyway – and that's an important asset for a captain. You must be able to issue orders when required, and to offer encouragement when necessary.

It's mainly when play stops that I find myself more involved than usual. If a player is injured, for example . . . or if I feel I should mention some aspect of the game to the referee.

I know that some people say that a striker, or a goalkeeper, should never be a team leader because they are essentially 'lonely' players who are often expected to 'do their own thing'.

Personally, I don't agree with this at all. I've known some terrific

'keepers who have made great skippers. And I certainly haven't found that being a striker affects my captaincy in the slightest.

Anyway, at international level every player is capable of leading the team and making important decisions.

Although it may be a bit of a cliché to say so, an England side is virtually a team of eleven captains with everyone shouting and encouraging!

That makes my job a whole lot easier and a whole lot more enjoyable!

GARY'S CAPTAINS

Throughout his career Gary has served under some fine skippers: "The main captains during my seven seasons with Leicester City were MARK WALLINGTON – a prime example of a goalkeeper making a good skipper – and Northern Ireland international JOHN O'NEILL.

"KEVIN RATCLIFFE was my captain at Everton in 1985–86 when we finished as League and Cup runners-up to Liverpool. The previous season Kevin had led the Blues to the Championship.

"My skipper at Barcelona was JOSE ALEXANCO, while Spurs are led by the excellent GARY MABBUTT.

"With England I've served under BRYAN ROBSON, PETER SHILTON and TERRY BUTCHER."

Another goal for Gary . . . as usual in the right place at the right time to score against Hungary at Wembley in 1990.

CHRIS WOODS
RANGERS

A t international level Chris Woods has had to wait a long time to become England's number one goalkeeper – thanks to a certain Peter Shilton who played at the highest level until he was 40!

But at Nottingham Forest, Woods was a League Cup winner . . . before he had played a League game!

In 1977/78 Shilts joined Forest from Stoke but was Cup-tied. So Woods came in for League Cup games and helped Forest win the tournament.

Woods, frustrated by the presence of Shilton (it was not to be the only time in his career) moved to QPR and then Norwich, establishing himself in the England squad but as the virtual permament understudy to Shilton.

His big break came in 1986 when Graeme Souness paid £1 million to take him to Glasgow Rangers and "McWoods", as he is affectionately known, has shared in the Light Blues' successes over the past few years.

NIGEL JEMSON

FOREST

Nottingham Forest boss Brian Clough often jokes that he is a bad judge of a player. So when Cloughie's greengrocer recommended a young Preston forward, the Forest manager sent his scouts to watch the lad.

Now, Nigel Jemson is another gem in Clough's crown – thanks to the man who supplies his fruit and vegetables!

In 1989/90, the Preston-born forward achieved every player's dream by scoring the winning goal at Wembley. Jemson's goal was decisive as Forest beat Oldham 1-0 to win the Littlewoods Cup and since then his unpredictable skills have made him a favourite with the City Ground regulars.

Jemson had a relatively slow start to his Forest career, being loaned to Bolton and back to Preston while he learnt his trade.

But Jemson is now almost the finished article . . . quick, good on the ball, excellent dribbling ability and able to do the unexpected.

With a name like Marco Gabbiadini, you would half expect to see the striker playing for Juventus or Inter Milan. He may one day . . . but at the moment the Nottingham-born Sunderland star is the pin-up boy of Roker Park. Gabbiadini's family may be Italian but Marco is English through and through . . . despite his name! He's been capped at England Under-21 level after his goal exploits with York and Sunderland rocketed him into the international forefront. Gabbiadini began his career with York where he prospered under manager Denis Smith. When Smith joined Sunderland, Gabbiadini followed and responded by topping the Roker goal-chart in his first three seasons. He scored 21 goals as Sunderland were promoted to the First Division in 1990 and it quickly became obvious that this crowd-pleaser was not out of his depth at the highest level. Gabbiadini is quick, has super control, can lose his marker and has a good eye for goal. Gabbiadini reads the game brilliantly, which means he is usually one move ahead of most players. Will Italy beckon? Perhaps . . . but Sunderland supporters hope it will be only for an international or a European tie!

MARCO GABBIADINI
SUNDERLAND

ROBERT ROSARIO

NORWICH

Robert Rosario may well be the only First Division player with an O level in sculpture.

It isn't just that which makes the Hammersmith-born centre-forward stand out. The 6ft 3in striker of Portuguese origin is also one of the most accomplished forwards in the League, a player who leads his line superbly. Norwich picked him up from non-League Hillingdon Borough and as he developed through the ranks at Carrow Road it soon became obvious that he was a player of genuine class. Rosario made his League debut in 1983/84 and was later loaned to Wolves to give him more experience.

He has tasted relegation to Division Two and promotion back to the First Division but always Norwich placed the emphasis on good attacking football.

Rosario acknowledges that he is fortunate to have a manager like Dave Stringer who puts the emphasis on entertainment and this suits the lanky striker who is one of the most unselfish players in the League.

His talents have been recognised by England at Under-21 level and the player with the O level in sculpture is happy with the way his career is shaping up!

GORDON STRACHAN

LEEDS UNITED

Gordon Strachan has been lucky enough to win a host of domestic and European honours with Dundee, Aberdeen, Manchester United and Leeds . . . but the wee Scot is still as ambitious as ever as he nears the twilight of his illustrious career. Strachan will be remembered as one of the finest ball-players ever produced by Scotland – and your dad will tell you they have produced a few in their time! Much of his career has involved Alex Ferguson, his manager at Aberdeen – where the Dons won the European Cup Winners' Cup – and Manchester United. In fact, many United fans still rue the day when Strachan was allowed to leave Old Trafford for an almost giveaway £300,000 to help Leeds re-establish themselves in Division One. At Elland Road, Strachan showed that there was still plenty of football left in him – to such an extent that he was recalled to the Scotland side in 1991 aged 34! There is a saying that great players don't get older . . . they become more experienced. And Strachan seems to have improved as the years go on. He is as fit now as he was when he made his Scottish League debut for Dundee back in 1974/75 – before many of you were born! Strachan has looked after himself, watching what he eats and drinks and training hard. Few would argue that Strachan is one of the classiest players of the modern era.

STEVE BULL
WOLVES

At school, no-one likes a bully . . . but at Wolves they love the Molineux Bully! Steve Bull, that is . . . who inflicts pain on defences most weeks with his goalscoring feats. There were doubts that Bull could score at the highest level but goals for England's Under-21's, the B team and the full side have made those claims nonsense. Yet Steve was almost given away by West Brom in 1986/87 – what a great bit of business it was when Graham Turner paid £25,000 to take him to Wolves. Since then it's been promotion and goals all the way as Bull and Andy Mutch formed a strike-partnership as lethal as any twosome in the League. Bobby Robson could not ignore the international claims of Bull who made four appearances for England in the 1990 World Cup Finals. Bull is simply a natural goalscorer, a player who comes alight near goal. There is nothing fancy about Bull's play but give him a sniff of goal and the chances are the ball will end up in the back of the net.

DAVID ROCASTLE
ARSENAL

They call David Rocastle "Rocky" at Arsenal . . . and the Gunner certainly packs a punch when he shoots for goal! His brilliant wing play has made him one of the crowd's favourites at Highbury and the regulars who have watched his progress through the juniors and reserves know his commitment to the club. Rocastle has been unlucky with injuries but the former Arsenal Player of the Year keeps bouncing back to show his wide range of skills. The Londoner has won England Under-21 and full caps while he has shared in Arsenal's Championship and Cup triumphs under George Graham. Rocky has created countless goals with his mazy dribbling and has weighed in with his own share, too. Continental clubs are eyeing him, too.

PAUL McSTAY

CELTIC

Paul McStay is still relatively unknown South of the Border, but the Celtic captain, who has completed his half century of caps for Scotland, is reckoned by many critics to be the most accomplished player in the Premier Division. McStay has won a host of individual honours for his classy midfield play despite the frustrations of Celtic and Scotland to really do themselves justice on the big stage in recent years. Since McStay made his debut as a promising teenager in 1981/82 it has been clear that Celtic had unearthed a rare talent. By the age of 18 McStay was a first team regular and many Celtic supporters would now consider him to be one of the club's finest players of the modern era. Injuries permitting, McStay should complete 500 appearances for the Parkhead club in the not too distant future, while 100 international caps is not out of the question. McStay is the classic Scottish ball-player with glorious close control and a fearsome shot.

JOHN ROBERTSON

HEARTS

Some players seem to be born to play for one particular club and John Robertson is Hearts through and through. He was born in Edinburgh and joined Hearts as an apprentice, making his League debut in 1981/82. The record books show "one game, no goals" for that solitary appearance that season . . . but the record books now are considerably different. In his first full season Robbo netted 19 times and he has regularly ended the campaign around that mark . . . the sort of figure that would satisfy just about any striker. Not surprisingly, quite a few English clubs had been alerted to Robertson's goalscoring feats. In 1987/88 Hearts accepted Newcastle's offer of £750,000 but away from his familiar surroundings Robertson was not comfortable. He played only 12 League games for the North East club before Hearts bought him back for £750,000. The goals began to flow again . . . and they have barely stopped since. The year 1990 was a traumatic one for both player and club as Hearts sacked manager Alex MacDonald, to the disappointment of Robertson who made his feelings public. But he put those frustrations behind him when Joe Jordan was appointed Tynecastle boss and carried on doing what he does best – and regularly – scoring goals!

Tony Cottee became Britain's costliest transfer when Everton paid West Ham £2.2 million for him in 1988. That's a big tag for anyone to live up to but even if the Londoner hasn't claimed a regular first team spot at Goodison Park, Cottee has still shown his predatorial instincts when given the chance. Few players are as sharp as Cottee in the penalty area. He has the ability to turn away from his marker and shoot all in one movement . . . with deadly effect. West Ham fans remember him affectionately – not surprisingly as he averaged 17 goals a season at Upton Park during his career with the Hammers. Cottee has been capped at Youth, Under-21 and full level by England.

TONY COTTEE

EVERTON

DAVID PLATT

ASTON VILLA

David Platt has worked his way to the top the hard way. Given a free transfer by Manchester United as a youngster, he was handed another chance to make the grade with Crewe and in four seasons at Gresty Road emerged as a skilful forward with seemingly endless energy. Graham Taylor brought Platt to Aston Villa for a mere £200,000 in 1987/88 and it was here that his talent came to the fore. In 1989/90, playing just behind the main strikers, Platt scored 19 goals from an advanced midfield role as Villa finished in second place . . . almost inevitably behind Liverpool.

Platt was not a regular or assured of a place in the England side as the 1990 World Cup finals began, but in the Second Round tie against Belgium Platt scored the last gasp extra-time winner, volleying in Paul Gascoigne's free-kick. It was possibly the most spectacular goal of Italia 90 . . . a star was born. Under Taylor, who became England boss after the Finals, Platt has emerged as a key figure and Villa turned down multi-million bids from Italian clubs for this multi-talented star.

PROFILE
Kenny Dalglish

Not for the first time . . . Kenny Dalglish, Manager of the Year, 1990.

When Kenny Dalglish joined Celtic from Cumbernauld United as a hopeful youngster in 1967, no-one could have dreamed of the impact he would have on British soccer.

Now, King Kenny is recognised as one of the greatest players ever to play in Scotland and England while his achievements as manager of Liverpool, the club he once graced as a brilliant goalscorer, have already put him alongside the all-time greats.

Kenny may one day have his own Hall of Fame to accommodate all the trophies he has won. There is virtually nothing worth winning that Kenny hasn't won.

The Glasgow-born forward made 204 Scottish League appearances for Celtic, helping them to win six Championships, the Scottish Cup four times and the League Cup once.

But it was with Liverpool, whom he joined in 1977 in a £440,000 deal as successor to Kevin Keegan, that Kenny really hit the headlines throughout Europe.

Three European Cup winners' medals, six Championships, four League Cup medals, an FA Cup winners' medal – and more since he stopped being a player-manager and concentrated solely on managing!

Kenny could not have become manager of Liverpool at a more difficult time. He succeeded Joe Fagan in 1985 immediately after the Heysel tragedy, but the following season led the Reds to the League and FA Cup double . . . a feat no previous Anfield boss had achieved.

As a player Kenny was one of the most skilful and subtle forwards in the world, winning 102 caps for Scotland between 1972 and 1987.

Yet to outsiders Kenny never appeared management material. He is not an extrovert headline-seeker but someone who prefers to let his actions speak for him . . . and they have done that loud and clear!

It was a surprise when it was announced Kenny was the new manager of Liverpool but he went about the job in his own way.

Alan Hansen, Liverpool's skipper during their glory years of the Eighties, says: "The first day Kenny met the players as manager he told us the situation had changed and from now we should call him 'boss'.

"He had to show everyone he was in charge but he was able to do it with the right attitude."

It was a great shock then, when Dalglish suddenly resigned as manager. He is someone Liverpool will never, ever forget.

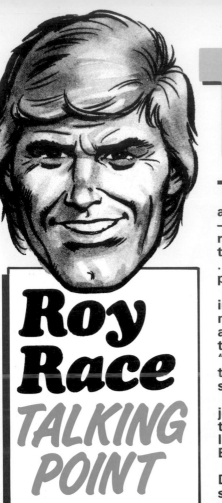

Roy Race
TALKING POINT

The two hardest jobs in soccer are scoring goals and being a manager. I know – I have to do both! So I realise just how difficult the task of the player-manager is . . . whichever position he plays.

As football moves steadily into the Nineties, the job of a manager is so complex. Gone are the days when the boss turned up for training, said "good morning, lads", went training, had a joke and a shower . . . and went home.

It's true to say that a boss's job is only half done when training is finished. I bet the likes of Peter Reid and Terry Butcher would agree.

It amazes me that Kenny Dalglish and Graeme Souness successfully played for and managed arguably the two biggest clubs in Britain – Liverpool and Glasgow Rangers. It's a wonder they ever had time to have a cup of tea!

A lot of people feel that the role of a player-manager is too much. That someone should either be a player or a manager, but not try to combine two jobs.

I can see both sides of the argument but as most examples that spring to mind have been successes, it seems to prove that the right man CAN combine the job of playing with that of managing his team-mates. I'm sure that Kenny, Graeme, Terry, Peter and every player-manager would agree with me when I say that the greatest thrill in football is playing . . . especially when you score lots of goals, as I've been lucky enough to do!

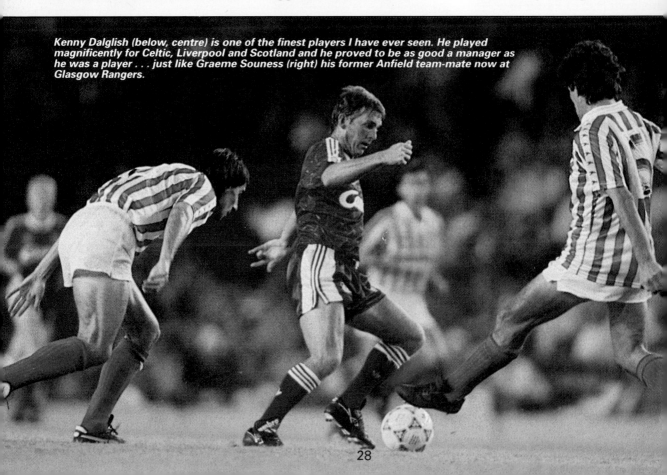

Kenny Dalglish (below, centre) is one of the finest players I have ever seen. He played magnificently for Celtic, Liverpool and Scotland and he proved to be as good a manager as he was a player . . . just like Graeme Souness (right) his former Anfield team-mate now at Glasgow Rangers.

OT SEAT

This is why players try to play for as long as possible. Just because they become a manager, they do not want to hang up their boots.

It can be a huge advantage to be out on the field with the lads, seeing things – both good and bad – first hand. A manager cannot really influence things from the dug-out. It's against the laws to yell instructions to players from the bench (we've all been guilty of doing this at one time or another, though!) but if a manager is out in the thick of the action, he can encourage his men without falling foul of the referee.

I must confess I was a little surprised when Liverpool appointed Kenny Dalglish as player-manager in 1985. Kenny has always been one

CONTINUED OVERLEAF

Terry Butcher, the Coventry player-manager, is one of the bravest defenders around.

As a player, Peter Reid has always led by example. Now he's doing the same as manager of Manchester City.

THE HOT SEAT

CONTINUED

of my favourite players but he never really struck me as a potential manager.

How wrong can you be? Since 1985, Liverpool have never been out of the Championship race, they've won the Double and Kenny could go down in history as not only one of the best players of all time . . . but also as one of the finest managers.

Liverpool are such a well-run club it should shock no-one they produce so many top bosses.

Graeme Souness has revolutionised Scottish soccer in his time at Ibrox Park. Okay, he's spent heavily but spending millions doesn't guarantee success.

However, Graeme has invested wisely and has been rewarded with enough silverware to ensure overtime for the cleaners who have to polish Rangers' trophies!

Peter Reid and Terry Butcher joined the player-manager ranks in 1990/91. Peter learnt a lot under Howard Kendall at Manchester City and when Howard moved back to Everton, Peter was the popular choice.

On the field, Peter has always led by example. A

ABOVE . . . Former Liverpool right-back Phil Neal is doing a good job at Bolton.
LEFT . . . Things didn't work out too well for Trevor Francis at QPR but I'm sure he'll be a top boss one day.

never-say-die midfielder, he fought back from a series of injuries to play for England in the 1986 World Cup finals.

He's taken those positive qualities to the hot seat and I'm sure Peter will be as successful as a manager as he was a player.

The same applies to Terry Butcher who became one of the most popular players with the Rangers supporters as captain of the Glasgow giants.

Has there ever been a braver defender? I'd have him in my back-four any day – that way I wouldn't have to play against him!

Phil Neal, another Liverpool old boy, has been doing a splendid job at Bolton – it isn't easy managing a club from the lower divisions in the north west in the shadow of the big Manchester and Merseyside clubs.

Some players haven't had quite the success they would have hoped for. Things didn't work out for Trevor Francis at Queens Park Rangers, although I'm sure Trevor will one day become a top boss. He has impressed me when I've heard him talk on television – he speaks a lot of sense.

If a player wants to become a manager should he start at a smaller club, like Brian Flynn did with Wrexham . . . or go straight in at the deep

end with a big club?

It depends on the situation and the club. Working with limited resources at Wrexham isn't easy, as Brian Flynn would admit, but it's valuable experience and if the chance of managing a First Division club ever comes along, the former Welsh international will be all the better for sampling life in the Fourth Division.

Player-managers aren't new, of course. I remember Johnny Giles, who did both jobs at West Brom, playing for and managing the Republic of Ireland, too.

What a work load! That task would probably be too much for one person these days.

One of the biggest problems for the player-boss is when he is playing badly. If I've missed a couple of sitters in the first-half, how can I give one of the other players a ticking-off for not playing well?

The answer is that I have to separate the two jobs. When I'm on the field I'm a player – when I give a team-talk I'm a manager.

It can also be very embarrassing for player-managers when they are booked or, even worse, sent-off. But we should set the right example and not get into trouble with officials.

A player-manager must also be strong enough to drop himself if it is best for the side – either because he's playing badly or because a change of tactics is necessary.

I promise you, there is no greater thrill than playing, especially playing well.

It isn't easy for Brian Flynn to be player-manager at Wrexham, working with limited resources.

GOALKEEPER

THE BALL WAS HIT LIKE A ROCKET TOWARDS THE UNGUARDED NET...

YESSSSSS! IT'S GOING IN! IT'S **THERE**—!

A GOAL AT LAST—!

UUUUUHHHH!

CHEERS OF ANTICIPATION TURNED TO GASPS OF DISBELIEF!

HE—HE SAVED IT!

WHAT A **STOP**! THAT WAS NOTHING SHORT OF MIRACULOUS!

TRUST RICK STEWART! HE ALWAYS MANAGES TO PERFORM THE IMPOSSIBLE!

YOU ALL RIGHT, RICK? HURT YOUR WRIST?

JUST GAVE IT A BANG WHEN I LANDED, THAT'S ALL.

34

FEELING OKAY YET, RICK?

YES. JUST HALF DROWNED, THAT'S ALL!

TYNEFIELD FINISHED TRIUMPHANT...

WELL PLAYED, RICK, YOU KNOW WHAT THEY SAY : "YOU'VE GOT TO BE MAD TO BE A GOALKEEPER!"

YOU'VE GOT TO BE MADE OF IRON, I KNOW THAT!

BUT RICK'S RUN OF INJURIES CONTINUED...

OH, THAT WAS A FINE SAVE BY THE GOALKEEPER!

HOW DID HE GET ACROSS TO THAT ONE? I THOUGHT IT WAS PAST HIM!

...HEN...

RICK! WHAT HAVE YOU KICKED IT INTO TOUCH FOR?

MY FINGER, JASON. THE ONE I DISLOCATED BEFORE. GUESS WHAT—?

OOUUCCHH!

THAT'S BACK!

HE'S AS TOUGH AS THEY COME, BOSS. MOST PLAYERS WOULD HAVE GONE OFF TO HOSPITAL WITH THAT. NOT OUR RICK!

THE KNOCKS HE'S TAKING THESE DAYS MAKES ME THINK HE'S INJURY PRONE...

UUUUHHHH!

OOOOFFF!

WELL BLOCKED, RICK!

THAT WAS TRAVELLING. IT ALMOST MADE A HOLE IN HIM!

BEFORE LONG, THE ENTIRE TEAM WAS JOINING IN A LEG-PULLING EXERCISE!

SURE YOU DON'T NEED A WHEELCHAIR, RICK!

YOU'RE PICKING UP MORE INJURIES THAN A STUNT MAN—AND THEY GET PAID!

BUT THE GOALMOUTH INCIDENT IN THE FOLLOWING GAME WAS NOT FUNNY...

THEIR STRIKER'S CLEAR!

IT'S ONE AGAINST ONE... HE'S ONLY GOT RICK TO BEAT!

HE'S SPARK OUT. HE CAUGHT HIS HEAD ON MY KNEE.

UUURRRGGHH!

BRAVE SAVE, GOALIE! HE WAS DETERMINED TO GET THE BALL AND HE DIDN'T WORRY ABOUT GETTING HURT!

THEY SHOULD CALL HIM FEARLESS STEWART!

CONCUSSED! HE'S GOT TO COME OFF, REF.

N-NO! I'M ALL RIGHT. I CAN PLAY ON—

RICK WAS EXAMINED BY THE CLUB DOCTOR...

YOU'D BETTER TAKE A REST FROM THE NEXT GAME, RICK. THAT WAS A NASTY KNOCK...

BUT I'M FINE, DOC! HONEST I AM! I WANT TO PLAY...

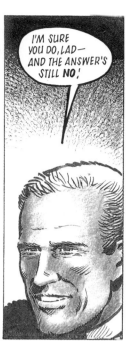

I'M SURE YOU DO, LAD— AND THE ANSWER'S STILL NO!

AND SO...

CHEER UP, RICK. DAVE SAUNDERS IS A GOOD 'KEEPER. HE WON'T LET US DOWN COVERING FOR YOU FOR JUST ONE GAME.

I GUESS YOU'RE RIGHT, JOHN.

MIDWAY THROUGH THE FIRST HALF...

THAT'S A GOOD CROSS INTO THE AREA...

DAVE SAUNDERS IS COMING FOR IT... HE'S SAFE IN THE AIR...

WELL TAKEN 'KEEPER!

BUT AS THE RESERVE GOALKEEPER LANDED...

I DON'T BELIEVE IT! SURELY HE'S NOT CROCKED HIMSELF!

AAAHHH!

BAD! COULD BE TORN LIGAMENTS!

MANAGER JOHN ROCKWELL CALLED A CRISIS MEETING...

RICK WILL BE FIT FOR THE NEXT GAME, BUT WE'VE GOT NO COVER. WE NEED ANOTHER GOALKEEPER **DESPERATELY!** I WANT EVERYONE TO KEEP THEIR EYES OPEN...

TWO DAYS LATER...

I'VE FOUND HIM, RICK! A GOALKEEPER! HE'S BRILLIANT! DOWN AT THE SCHOOL PLAYING FIELD. WE'VE JUST GOT TIME...

CALM DOWN, JASON... I'M COMING...

THAT'S HIM, RICK. THE TALL LAD. YOU WAIT AND SEE...

LOOK AT **THAT,** RICK! A SUPER SAVE, WASN'T IT?

IT WAS, JASON. YOU'RE RIGHT. HE'S A REAL FIND.

WHEN THE GAME FINISHED...

YOU– YOU WANT ME TO PLAY FOR **TYNEFIELD'S YOUTH TEAM?** BUT I'M NOT **REALLY** A GOALKEEPER. I ONLY WENT IN BECAUSE NO-ONE ELSE WOULD...AND I WAS TALL...

IT TAKES A GOALKEEPER TO RECOGNISE A GOALKEEPER. I'M SAYING YOU'VE GOT THE TALENT TO MAKE THE GRADE. BELIEVE ME...

THE YOUNG GOALKEEPER'S NAME WAS TONY BELL...

HE'S GOOD...BUT I STILL CAN'T CONVINCE HIM. BEING THROWN IN AT THE DEEP END MAY BE THE ONLY WAY...

YOU RECK'N THEN HE'LL REALISE HE'S GOOD ENOUGH..?

COME ON, RICK— DON'T JUST STAND THERE! LET'S HAVE A FEW SHOTS AT YOU...

SAAVVEEDD!

NICE ONE, RICK!

AAAHH! MY KNEE... MY KNEE...

IT SEEMS ALL RIGHT, RICK. NO SWELLING YET...

I CAN'T BEND IT EASILY. I KNOW I SHAN'T BE ABLE TO PLAY TOMORROW...

ROY OF THE RANGERS

Imagine having this choice: do I play for the World Champions . . . the 1994 World Cup hosts . . . or any of the four British teams?

Not an easy predicament – but that's exactly the situation that Queens Park Rangers' multi-national striker Roy Wegerle found himself in.

The South African-born star has a German passport because of his parents. He is eligible for the United States because his wife is American . . . and because of his time in Britain, Roy of the Rangers could also have the choice of England, Scotland, Wales or Northern Ireland.

Even Roy Race would envy that!

But whichever club or country Roy plays for can be guaranteed one thing . . . they have a brilliant striker at their disposal.

Roy was picked up for a nominal fee by Chelsea from the Tampa Bay Rowdies in the USA. For one reason or another they let him go to Luton for £80,000 in 1988 but within a season and a half Roy's displays had rocketed him into the £1 million bracket.

Don Howe was happy to make Roy a soccer millionaire and at QPR he showed just what a brilliant player he is.

His speed, control and finishing put him among the First Division's best in 1990/91 and Roy's future looks as bright as Roy Race's!

42

TAYLOR
England's new boss

Even at the age of five Graham Taylor was showing the sort of skills that would later make him manager of England.

Teachers at Henderson Avenue School in Scunthorpe remember him organising playground matches . . . a talent that has taken him to the top of his profession.

When Bobby Robson stepped down from the most demanding – but most prestigious – job in English soccer Graham Taylor was the obvious choice.

Taylor's public relations were excellent – as the son of a journalist he learnt how to handle the Press, who can make or break a manager.

It was no surprise when Taylor was officially named as Robson's successor after England's successful World Cup campaign in 1990 when they reached the semi-finals.

Yet Taylor's early days in soccer were far from glamorous. He signed for Grimsby as a 16-year-old full-back and played 189 games for them.

He joined Lincoln and made 152 League appearances for the Imps before his career came to a premature end during a game at Northampton in February, 1972.

In a freak accident,

Graham Taylor likes to visit League clubs and here he enjoys a training session with Southampton.

GRAHAM TAYLOR

Taylor severely damaged a hip when he kicked the ground instead of the ball. A specialist told him that if he did not quit playing football there was every chance he would be in a wheelchair by the age of 40.

Taylor had always been a keen student of the game and joined Lincoln's coaching staff. When manager David Herd was sacked, he applied for the job and at 28 became the youngest boss in the Football League. What's more, he had to take a pay cut!

His start as a manager was hardly successful . . . Lincoln lost their first 11 matches under Taylor and he feared his managerial career could be over before it had really begun.

He recalls: "With a young family, a duff hip and a big mortgage I

The man who cares passionately about the game and has at last achieved the pinnacle of success – manager of England!

quickly learnt about pressure."

Taylor quickly learnt about being a manager, too. He gradually changed Lincoln's fortunes and in 1976 they won the Fourth Division.

Even in those days Taylor was a strict disciplinarian. He once fined himself £20 for running on the pitch to yell at one of his players.

In 1977, Taylor joined Watford whose pop star chairman Elton John had the same ambitions as his young manager . . . to take the Hornets to the top.

When Taylor took charge Watford were in the Fourth Division. By the time he left in 1987 they had established themselves as a top club.

Taylor had similar success at Aston Villa.

Villa were reluctant to lose Taylor but they realised they could not stand in his way when the call came for him to manage England.

After all, Graham had always been Taylor-made for the job!

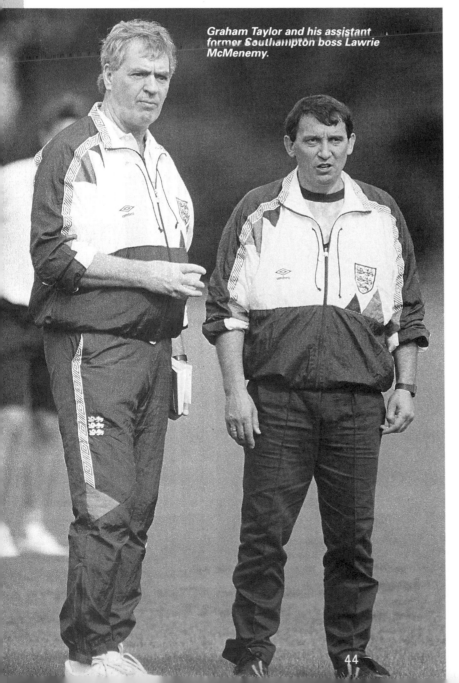

Graham Taylor and his assistant former Southampton boss Lawrie McMenemy.

DIAL FOR DANGER!

9

Brian McClair has proved to be a regular goalscorer in Scotland and England with Celtic and Manchester United.

Warning – these men are dangerous. They can hurt your defence! Do not tackle them alone . . . two defenders are usually necessary to stop their progress towards goal!

The Football League has a history of great players wearing the number nine shirt, going back to Bobby Charlton, Nat Lofthouse and other stars of yesteryear.

Their modern day successors are every bit as good. While defences have become better organised and more difficult to beat, attackers of the Nineties are faster, more mobile . . . and deadlier.

Take Brian McClair, for example. Few people remember that he began his career with Aston Villa but they allowed him to leave for Motherwell in 1981 without playing a League game.

McClair's potential was spotted by Celtic and two seasons later the Bellshill-born forward was wearing the famous green-and-white of the Parkhead team.

The goals flowed and McClair was snapped up by Manchester United for a bargain £850,000 in 1987 . . . one of the shrewdest bits of business by Alex Ferguson.

Twenty-four goals in his first season in English football is proof that McClair adapted with ease and now his partnership with Mark Hughes is among the best in Britain.

Alan Smith may have a common surname . . . but his talent is very rare! The Arsenal striker has been a consistent goalscorer throughout his career and the £800,000 George Graham paid Leicester for him in 1986 was a snip.

Smith tends not to score spectacular goals but like another North London striker, Gary Lineker, is in the right place at the right time to supply the right touch.

Mick Quinn was an apprentice at Derby before joining Wigan. He cracked 19 goals in 69 League games before moving on to Stockport in 1982 (39 goals in 63 games). The following year he was on the way to Oldham (34 in 80). Portsmouth was Quinn's next port of call in 1985 (54 in 121) and four years later he was on his way to Newcastle where he smashed in 32 League goals last season.

Kerry Dixon was an apprentice at Tottenham but failed to make the grade at White Hart Lane and after a spell at non-League Dunstable he joined Reading in 1980. The 29-year-old striker hit 51 goals in 116 League appearances for The Royals before joining Chelsea in 1983. He has scored over 130 League goals for the Stamford Bridge club. Made his senior England debut against Mexico in 1985 and has won eight caps.

A common name but a rare talent . . . Arsenal striker Alan Smith.

Heads he wins . . . Newcastle United centre-forward Mick Quinn.

Chelsea's Kerry Dixon – who resembles Roy Race – takes on Sunderland's Kevin Ball. The blond number 9 has won eight England caps.

Lee Chapman has played for Stoke, Arsenal, Sunderland, Sheffield Wednesday, Nottingham Forest and Leeds, as well as Niort in France and wherever he's been, the goals have flowed.

Chapman's goals helped Leeds re-establish themselves in the First Division in 1990/91 . . . Lee is one of those natural goalscorers who will punish any lapse in concentration by a defence.

Son of another number nine, Mark Hateley has scored lots of goals in

Wherever he has played Lee Chapman has been a regular goalscorer.

Celtic's Dariusz Dziekanowski . . . known simply as Jacki to the fans.

England, Italy and Scotland. Very sharp in the area, defenders can't afford to take their eyes off him.

Dariusz Dziekanowski is known simply as Jacki at Celtic – imagine the problems if someone on the terraces began chanting "give us a D . . . !!!"

The Pole is a forward with the sort of speed that takes him away from defenders and creates chances out of nothing.

It is the speed and power of Cyrille Regis that have made the Coventry centre-forward a regular goalscorer during the Seventies (with WBA), Eighties and Nineties.

Talent runs in the family – brother John is a world-class sprinter for Britain.

But one player who will justifiably be called an all-time great is Ian Rush, who has re-written the history books.

It's been goals and more goals for Rushie and his number nine shirt has become the most famous sight for defenders . . . that's all they see as he races away!

Mark Hateley has scored a multitude of goals in England and Italy. He is currently with Rangers.

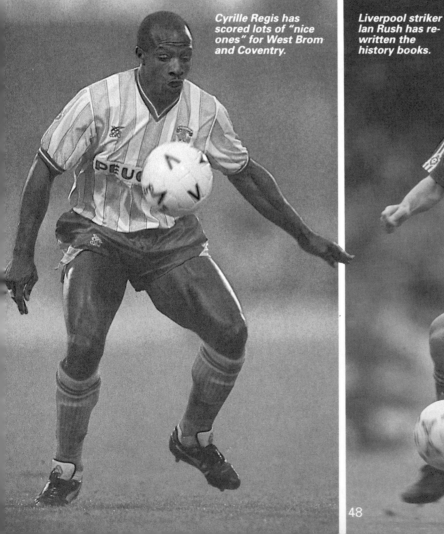

Cyrille Regis has scored lots of "nice ones" for West Brom and Coventry.

Liverpool striker Ian Rush has re-written the history books.

WRIGHT & BRIGHT

Palace terror twins

On the ball as usual . . . Ian Wright.

Their names sound alike and their business is the same . . . and Crystal Palace hope opposing defenders are confused as Ian Wright and Mark Bright bear down on them.

They're the stars of the Palace but they don't get a 21 gun salute – more like a 21 GOAL salute!

Wright and Bright are the terror twins of Selhurst Park. Almost everything about the pair is similar.

They joined Palace in

Wright's partner in goals, Mark Bright.

49

Mark Bright and Derby's Mick Forsyth challenge for a high ball.

WRIGHT & BRIGHT

the mid-Eighties as little known players. They both play up front. But most important of all, Ian and Mark are usually . . .on the mark!

Their first full season together with Palace was 1987/88 when Wright scored 20 goals and Bright netted 25.

The following season the "score" was Ian 24, Mark 20, as Palace returned to the First Division.

In 1989/90 Wright broke a leg and managed only eight goals but Bright scored 12 as Palace established a sound base back in the top flight.

It was also the season the Eagles scored high in the FA Cup . . . and landed at Wembley!

Wright was injured in March and hadn't started a League game so manager Steve Coppell left him on the subs bench for the final against Manchester United – Coppell's old club.

Rarely has a sub had such a dramatic effect. In the first game Wright climbed from the bench to score twice as Palace came from behind to

A right royal striker – Palace's Ian Wright.

draw 3-3.

In the replay Wright again started as a sub but this time there was no repeat performance as United won 1-0 . . . but Wright had shown a world-wide audience what he could do.

Bright, born in Stoke, began his career with Port Vale before joining Leicester. The goals never really flowed at Filbert Street – only six in 42 League games – but Steve Coppell saw enough in Bright to invest the modest sum of £70,000.

Coppell wouldn't sell Mark for 10 times that amount now. Bright was a victim of the boo boys at Leicester but he's been elected Palace's Player of the Year as his partnership with Wright developed into what many people consider the best strike-force in the League.

Wright's arrival at Selhurst Park was even more modest – he didn't cost a penny!

PARK FOOTBALL

Ian was playing for a side called Ten-en-Bee in the Premier Division of the London and Kent Border League.

It was what you know as park football, where the players change in cars by the side of the pitch and afterwards have to go home for a bath.

Hardly glamorous but it was the level of football you, your pals or brother – even perhaps your dad – play in now. The moral is – you never know who is watching you so if you try your best anything might happen . . . ask Ian Wright.

Ian was saved from the dole queue by Steve Coppell's offer of a chance at Palace. The other offers on the table were from non-League Greenwich Borough or Dulwich Hamlet.

It took Ian about one and a half seconds to make up his mind. He had always wanted to be a professional footballer but thought the chance had passed him by. How wrong can you be?

When unknown players join

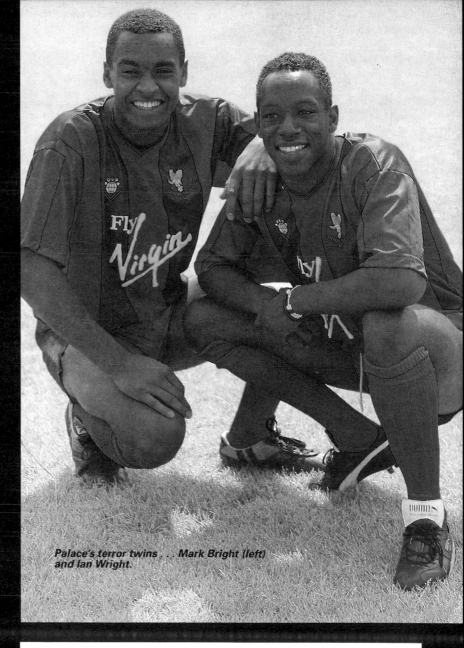

Palace's terror twins . . . Mark Bright (left) and Ian Wright.

Their names sound alike – their business is the same. Goal scoring!

a big club they are often in awe of the seniors. Not Ian – right away he was keen to show everyone what he could do . . . which was to score goals regularly.

Having established himself as a respected First Division striker, the greatest moment in his career came on February 6th, 1991, when he won his first full England

cap against Cameroon.

As Ian walked out of the tunnel at Wembley to the roar of the 60,000 crowd those days of Sunday morning football must have seemed a million miles away.

Wright and Bright will be back at Wembley in the future . . . either as the terror twins of Crystal Palace or wearing the white shirts of England.

THE EURO SCE

Probably the most famous hairstyle in world football . . . Ruud Gullit, the AC Milan and Holland forward.

Michael Laudrup almost joined Liverpool a few years ago.

The mass coverage of the World Cup, European Championship and European club competitions . . . plus the hundreds of foreign stars who have come to Britain in the past 15 years . . . has meant that our soccer fans are able to talk about the likes of Ruud Gullit and Jesper Olsen with as much authority as they could home-based stars.

We've seen Ossie Ardiles, Arnold Muhren, Hans Gillhaus . . . many top overseas stars . . . displaying their skills in the English and Scottish Leagues.

The success of the Home countries in the major international tournaments has enabled us to see all of the world's best players regularly in our living rooms . . . thanks to television.

From Roger Milla's World Cup wiggle to Ruud Gullit's dreadlocks – the stars of Africa, Europe and South America are familiar visitors.

Even supporters of England and the Republic of Ireland, who had to play Holland in the 1990 World Cup finals, were glad when Gullit, the brilliant AC Milan forward, had recovered from a knee injury to play in Italia 90.

Holland were a little disappointing . . . but Gullit showed that he was one of the greatest players in the world and returned home with his reputation enhanced.

Gullit cost Milan £5 million from PSV Eindhoven in

Holland but he has helped the Italians to the top of the tree in world football, winning the European Cup and the World Cup Championship.

We'll never see Gullit in the First Division, sadly . . . but Michael Laudrup was a whisker away from joining Liverpool a few years back.

The Great Dane had talks at Anfield but eventually opted for a career in Italy before

PEAN VE

Czechoslovakia's Ivo Knoflicek nearly became a Derby player.

A real star . . . Real Madrid's Romanian midfielder Gheorghe Hagi.

Portugal winger Paulo Futre reigns in Spain with Atletico Madrid.

players in the Spanish League where forwards have to be expert in the high jump to avoid some of the tackling!

Another star to reign in Spain is Real Madrid midfielder Gheorghe Hagi of Romania – singled out by Ireland boss Jack Charlton as the best player in Italia 90.

Hagi's passing and shooting ability were a feature of Romania's play and Real were happy to give him the chance to shine in the West.

Another star from the East now in the West is Ivo Knoflicek, who almost joined Derby a few seasons ago.

His speed down the wing would have brightened up the Baseball Ground but the Czechoslovakia ace eventually headed for Italy where, in the 1990 World Cup, he showed just what a good player he is.

A classy midfielder who has had a chequered career is Belgian born Enzo Scifo. He

moving to Barcelona. Laudrup will be remembered for his brilliant displays in the 1986 World Cup in Mexico –but at least Liverpool have the consolation of knowing that they could hardly have been more successful even if Laudrup had signed for them.

Portuguese ace Paulo Futre cost Atletico Madrid £2.3 million but the winger has proved to be one of the top

CONTINUED OVERLEAF

Enzo Scifo, Belgian-born midfielder with French club Auxerre, possesses that rare gift of skill on the ball.

53

Jurgen Klinsmann, Inter Milan's German striker, shows his skill in a European Championship tie against Italy.

Marco Goalo . . . Holland's Marco Van Basten.

CONTINUED

proved a disappointment with Internazionale in Italy after a much-heralded transfer from Anderlecht. Now with French club Auxerre, he has set his new country alight with his skills.

There are many great strikers in world football and few would doubt that West Germany's Jurgen Klinsmann was a crucial part of his country's success in winning the 1990 World Cup final.

He has the ability to shake off even the closest of markers and given even a quarter of a chance Klinsmann will punish any defence.

For Inter Milan, Klinsmann has been an outstanding forward against the best organised defences in Europe in the Italian League.

It's a similar story with Marco Van Basten, the former European Footballer of the Year who has been a European Champion with Holland and AC Milan.

Marco Goalo can score the most spectacular of goals . . . or tap in the simplest of chances. He's powerful in the air and lethal on the ground.

He has the knack of scoring the all-important goals in the vital matches.

Before the 1990 World Cup, Toto Schillaci was relatively unknown. He wasn't even in Italy's starting line-up at the beginning of the tournament but by the end his six goals made him the competition's top striker.

The Juventus star was unstoppable in Italia 90 . . . coming from nowhere to take the world by storm.

A quiet person, Toto said he did not like being in the spotlight but with his ability he became the centre of attention for every television crew and newspaper reporter

in Italy.

Dragan Stojkovic had agreed a £5 million transfer from Red Star Belgrade to Chris Waddle's Marseille shortly before the 1990 World Cup.

He had a lot to live up to but as the competition progressed the Yugoslavia midfielder showed the qualities that had made him one of the costliest players in the world.

A free kick specialist, the Magic Dragan was brilliant but soon after joining Marseille sustained a knee injury that forced him to miss most of the 1990/91 season.

There are many more stars from around the world who have become household names in Britain – and we in Britain are lucky enough to have our own stars who are as good as the best in the world!

Toto Schillaci of Italy was the leading goalscorer in the 1990 World Cup Finals.

ON THE BALL

SIX FIX

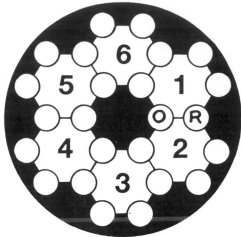

Solve the clues and write the six-letter answers round the numbers in the grid. You can go in any direction, and there's a two letter start.

1 First name of either Mr Rosario or Mr Fleck.
2 First name of Dutch superstar defender Koeman.
3 QPR's ex-England left back Kenny.
4 Arsenal's young striker Paul.
5 Team of Scottish Saints.
6 Stamford _____, home of Chelsea.

STRIKERGRAM

Re-arrange the letters to spell out top class strikers.
1 RUIN ASH (Liverpool)
2 QUILL IN NAN (Man City)
3 LEO GLUG CHIN (Nott'm Forest)
4 ME PLAN EACH (Leeds)

NUTMEGGED

A trivia teaser!
Brian Clough at Nott'm Forest, Harry Redknapp at Bournemouth and Ken Brown at both Norwich and Plymouth did this! What special thing links these managers together? It's all about the players they selected . . . got it?

TIME TWISTER

Smile, please! No prizes for recognising this England hero . . . but when was this pic taken? Was it 15 years ago, 12 years ago, six years ago, last year or this year?

ALL CHANGE

There are SIX changes between the pictures . . . can you spot the lot?

56

SNAKES AND LADDERS

Put yourself on the START position of our ladder, then move UP one space each time you answer a question correctly, and move DOWN one space each time you get an answer wrong.

Where will you finish up? Check your rating in this just-for-fun quick quiz!

1 Mark Falco, Paul Parker and Ray Wilkins all play for which London side?
2 Who was England's first choice 'keeper in Italia '90?
3 Who plays home games at Plough Lane?
4 What was the name of Scotland's manager in Italia '90?
5 Which team does NOT play in red: Liverpool, Manchester Utd, Nott'm Forest, Wolves.

RATING		
A CHAMP!	E Average	H Relegation stuff!
B Top Class	START No move	I Double relegation
C Very good	F Off form	J There's only way way to go!!!
D Good display	G Sliding down	

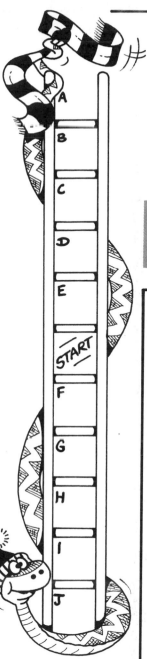

BLANKETY BLANK

Try to fill in the blanks.

1 Blackburn Rovers took on mighty Liverpool in the Third Round of the ___ Cup in January 1991. There was controversy at Ewood _____ when Blackburn's Eire centre half Kevin _____ was sent off, and then Liverpool's Glenn _____ went the same way. Simon _____ put Blackburn in the lead but tragedy struck when – in the last minute – Mark Atkins scored an _____ goal.

2 The 1990 World Cup Final between West _____ and Argentina was a very poor game. The South Americans had ___ players sent off and lost to a late goal from left-back Andy _____ who scored from a _____ .

3 In the televised live game from White _____ Lane between Spurs and Manchester Utd, England's midfield hero Paul _____ was sent off. After penalties from Tottenham's Gary _____ and United's _____ Bruce, Scottish striker Brian _____ won the game for the Manchester team.

ANSWERS BELOW (No cheating!)

STEPS

Answers go across in the step shaped grid.

1 What is the first name of Walsh and Stewart of Spurs?
2 Which club does Mark Wright play for?
3 At which road do Norwich City play home games?
4 Which London side play at Highbury?
5 Manchester United play at which 'Old' ground?
6 Which club has Kevin Keegan, Phil Neal and Alan Hansen as former captains?
7 Which Mel has played fullback for Sheffield Wednesday and Leeds?
8 Which Scottish side have played Englishmen Woods, Steven, Stevens and Spackman?
9 Which England winger John started his career with Watford?
10 What is the first name of Villa's England midfielder Platt?
11 What word goes with Ham and Bromwich Albion?

Keeping 'en

RIGHT
Liverpool's Bruce Grobbelaar may be unorthodox . . . but his brilliant goalkeeping has helped Liverpool to win many trophies.

They're the men who break forwards' hearts . . . but every great team has a great goalkeeper. Here we pay tribute to some of the men who thrill the fans – and frustrate opponents!

58

out!

OPPOSITE PAGE, BELOW
The man who has rewritten the goalkeeping record books – England's Peter Shilton, the world's most-capped player with 125 caps.
LEFT
Erik Thorstvedt, Spurs' Norwegian 'keeper, tips the ball to safety with an acrobatic leap.
BELOW, LEFT
Rated by many as the best goalkeeper in Britain – Neville Southall of Everton and Wales.
BELOW
Paddy Bonner, the Republic of Ireland's most-capped 'keeper, in action for Celtic against Rangers.

Keeping 'em out!

RIGHT
David Seaman became the most expensive goalkeeper in the world when he moved from Queens Park Rangers to Arsenal for £1.3 million during the summer of 1990. But he soon proved to be a bargain even at this price with a string of brilliant performances.

ABOVE
The arrival of £1 million Nigel Martyn from Bristol Rovers stiffened up the Crystal Palace defence.

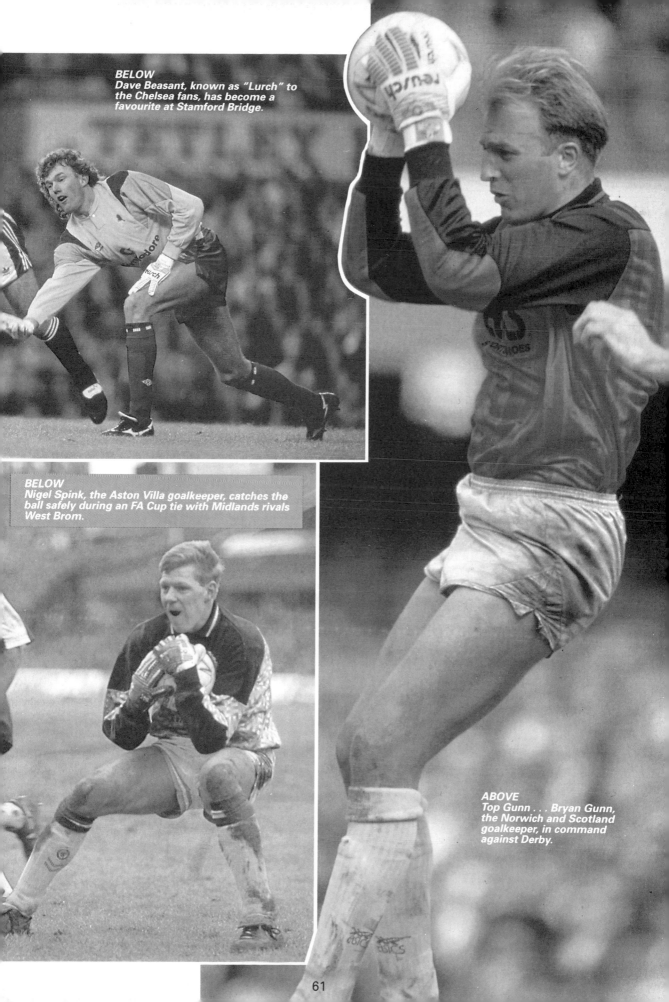

BELOW
Dave Beasant, known as "Lurch" to the Chelsea fans, has become a favourite at Stamford Bridge.

BELOW
Nigel Spink, the Aston Villa goalkeeper, catches the ball safely during an FA Cup tie with Midlands rivals West Brom.

ABOVE
Top Gunn . . . Bryan Gunn, the Norwich and Scotland goalkeeper, in command against Derby.

FRANZ BECKENBAUER

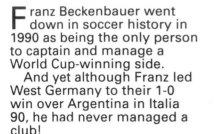

F ranz Beckenbauer went down in soccer history in 1990 as being the only person to captain and manage a World Cup-winning side.

And yet although Franz led West Germany to their 1-0 win over Argentina in Italia 90, he had never managed a club!

As a player Franz oozed style. Like England's Bobby Moore, he never seemed hurried and was so versatile that he played with stunning effect both in midfield and in defence.

Franz was the inspiration behind Bayern Munich's success during the Seventies when they won the European Cup in 1974, 1975 and 1976.

He had burst on the scene as a 19-year-old and after only 27 senior appearances for Bayern made his international debut aged 20.

A year later Franz appeared in the 1966 World Cup Final when he marked Bobby Charlton as England won 4-2 after extra time.

It was a rare disappointment in a glorious career. In 1972 Franz captained the Germans to success in the European Championship and two years later he lifted the World Cup when Holland were beaten 1-0 in Munich.

With Bayern, he had won five Championships and four West German Cup-winning medals to go with his hat-trick of European Cup trophies – plus a European Cup Winners' Cup medal.

The 1972 and 1976 European Footballer of the Year moved to the New York Cosmos in the now defunct North American Soccer League after winning 103 caps.

Two more Championships came his way in the USA before Franz headed home to join Hamburg whom he helped to win the West German title in 1982.

The Kaiser, as he is known, retired and took over as manager of West Germany in 1984. It was a gamble because Franz had no experience at this level but he soon showed that what he could do as a player he could do as a manager.

The Germans were beaten 3-2 in the 1986 World Cup Final by Argentina but had their revenge four years later when Franz made football history.

He had announced before the 1990 finals in Italy that afterwards he would be stepping down to hand over to Berti Vogts whatever West Germany's fate . . . but his career in charge of his country could not have had a happier ending as Andy Brehme scored the match-winning penalty.

The semi-final, of course, had seen England lose to West Germany in a nail-biting finish. With the score after extra time standing at 1-1, the match went to a penalty shoot-out, and Franz's team emerged victorious.

Franz has been awarded the Cross of Merit for his services to football and such is his versatility that he could walk into virtually any job in world soccer . . . as a coach, a manager, a consultant, public relations man or just about anything.

Franz has that priceless quality of being a winner – and that makes him very much in demand as people's thoughts turn towards the 1994 World Cup Finals in the United States.

BRIT
ABROAD

John Aldridge can justifiably claim to be a Real striker . . . a Real Sociedad striker!

The Republic of Ireland star has proved that he can score goals at any level . . . from the Fourth to the First Division in England, on the international stage . . . and in Spain.

Aldo is a Have Goals Will Travel player. His journey started in Newport before Jim Smith took him to Oxford. John's prolific goalscoring attracted the attention of Liverpool and soon Aldo was scoring 26 goals in his first full season in 1987/88.

This average was maintained until Real Sociedad stepped in with an offer Liverpool couldn't refuse . . . £1 million.

Nigel Clough . . . the brilliant Nottingham Forest striker with the most famous dad in football. Brian is, of course, Forest's manager, but refers to his son as "the number nine."

qualified for a major international final, but in 1988 Ireland reached the European Championship Finals in West Germany.

In their opening game Jack had to plot the downfall of England – which he did. Ray Houghton headed the goal that gave the Irish a sensational 1-0 win over Bobby Robson's side in Stuttgart. Ireland were eventually beaten 1-0 by Champions Holland – but Jack's Jolly Green Army returned to a hero's welcome in Dublin.

Jack was made an Honorary Irishman but while he was happy, he wasn't satisfied . . . there was the little matter of the World Cup coming up.

The solid professionalism Jack had instilled into the Republic plus a team pattern that may not be pretty . . . but is pretty difficult to break down . . . saw Ireland reach Italia 90 safely.

And who would be Ireland's first opponents again? England!

The game in Sardinia was never a classic but goals by Gary Lineker and Kevin Sheedy gave both countries a point.

Ireland may not have won a tie in Italia 90 – but draws against England, Egypt and Holland plus a penalty shootout over Romania put them in the quarter finals.

F A IRELAND

PROFILE

JACK CHARLTON

It is the luck of the Irish that they have Jack Charlton as manager!

When Jack took over as the Republic of Ireland's boss in February, 1986, they had a reputation of being underachievers.

Big Jack knew a thing or two about winning. As centre-half with Leeds he'd helped them win

trophies at home and in Europe – in 1966 he won a World Cup winners' medal with England.

Jack couldn't have had a worse start in charge of Ireland, though – they lost 1-0 at home to Wales. Since then, defeats – and goals against – have been very few and far between.

The Republic had never

But for a small country like the Republic to reach the last eight of the World Cup was a truly marvellous achievement.

The former manager of Middlesbrough, Sheffield Wednesday and Newcastle and the man who rates fishing almost as highly as football has certainly made his mark in world soccer.

GAZZA

He's called Gazza rather than Paul Gascoigne . . . he's known as a clown . . . but no-one has put a bigger smile on the face of football than the brilliant Tottenham and England midfielder.

He's the most talked about player in Britain. To many, he's also the most talented, a crowd-puller in the mould of George Best. And like the former Manchester United star, Gazza can do things on a football field many players only dream of.

Gazza is unorthodox both on and off the field. He's a natural for television and he comes across so well that when he retires from soccer, Terry Wogan had better watch out!

Some folk will tell you that present day players aren't as good as the footballers from yesteryear. If they do, reply: "What about Paul Gascoigne, then?" Chances are they'll be stumped for an answer.

Gazza was born in Gateshead on May 27th, 1967. He joined Newcastle – a club that has produced so many top players – as an apprentice and made his League debut for the

Gazza shows the all-action style that has made him a hero with Tottenham and England.

FROM PRINCE TO KING!

Magpies in 1984/85.

In three full seasons with Newcastle, Gazza showed that he had a very rare talent. Apart from creating goals, he was also a taker of goals . . . most of them memorable solo efforts.

He also showed himself to be a character, earning the nickname the Mars Bar Kid because of his liking for the chocolate bar. Fans used to turn up at games with Mars Bars but when Gazza realised he was eating too many, he went on a diet to slim down.

"I'm the Salad King now," he announced, patting his trim waistline.

A £2 million fee took him to Tottenham where much was expected of him. He has not disapponted and as he

BELOW
A tearful Paul Gascoigne applauds the England fans after the heartbreaking 5-4 penalty shoot-out loss to West Germany in the 1990 World Cup Finals.

RIGHT
A happier moment as Gazza celebrates the 3-2 win over Cameroon in the Quarter-Finals.

GAZZA

CONTINUED

On the ball . . . and shouting for the top . . . right on cue as usual . . . Paul Gascoigne.

Ah-ha, me hearties! "Long John" Gascoigne . . . the master of disguise!

worked his way up through the England Under-21 and B team it was obvious that full caps would come his way.

It was as a substitute against Denmark in 1989 that Gazza made his first appearance in a full England shirt. In 1990 he became a hero when television vividly captured his heartbreak against West Germany in the World Cup semi-final which England lost on penalties.

There was some doubt whether Gazza would be in Bobby Robson's starting line-up in Italia 90. Robson knew that to beat the best teams in the world you had to have the best players . . . and there were few

better than Paul Gascoigne.

In the early rounds he stamped his authority on the England team with some breathtaking displays. Over-enthusiasm meant he had collected a yellow card so he had to be careful against the Germans. One step out of line and he would miss the Final . . . if England got there.

Gazza was brilliant as England gave traditional rivals Germany their toughest game. But a mis-timed tackle on Thomas Berthold earned Gazza a second booking. He would miss England's next tie.

The tears of soccer's clown were there for everyone to see. Gazza could not hide his heartbreak, but he went on to play his heart out

LEFT . . . Why is Gazza so great? It's elementary, my deart Watson, says Paul "Sherlock Holmes" Gascoigne.
BELOW
How Gazza might have looked as a star of the 1890's.

as England eventually lost in the cruellest way – on penalties.

Gazza returned from Italy a national hero. Gazzamania was rampant – everyone wanted Paul on their show, in their paper or to open their shop.

He realised that nothing must interfere with his job and went on to score a hatful of goals in 1990/91.

The best of Gazza is yet to come. What we have seen already has made him one of the top players of modern times.

Everyone, it seems, has caught Gazzamania . . . but no-one is complaining!

HOT-SHOT HAMISH and MOUSE

HOT-SHOT HAMISH BALFOUR AND HIS PAL, KEVIN 'MIGHTY' MOUSE PLAYED FOR GLENGOW RANGERS IN THE SCOTTISH PREMIER DIVISION. JUST BEFORE CHRISTMAS THE DAILY POST NEWSPAPER ANNOUNCED A NEW COMPETITION...

THE BIGGEST CUP IN THE WORLD FOR THE HARDEST KICK IN FOOTBALL! OPEN TO ALL PROFESSIONALS!

YOU OUGHT TO GO IN FOR THIS, HAMISH— YOU'D WIN EASILY! NO-ONE COULD BEAT YOUR HOT-SHOT!

OCH, AWA', MON... I'D NO' GET ANYWHERE! ALL THE BEST PLAYERS WOULD ENTER!

I'D LIKE A REALLY BIG CUP, THOUGH. ALL I'VE EVER WON ARE A FEW CUPS FROM SCHOOL GAMES... AND ONE OR TWO CUP-WINNERS MEDALS AND LEAGUE CHAMPIONSHIPS...

THEY ASKED THE RANGERS' BOSS...

YE WANT TO ENTER SOME CRACKPOT KICKING CONTEST NEXT SATURDAY? NO WAY, MON... YE'RE PLAYING AGAINST HIBWELL ROVERS! IT'S A VITAL LEAGUE MATCH FOR US!

OCH, I ONLY ASKED...

HERE THEY COME! GOOD OLD RANGERS! HURRAHHH!

I SUPPOSE THE BOSS WAS RIGHT! THE CLUB COMES FIRST!

HE COULD HAVE GIVEN YOU A DAY OFF! IT'S A SHAME!

AFTER THE GAME STARTED...

I'LL TRY TO GIVE HAMISH A GOOD PASS SO HE CAN SCORE! IT'LL CHEER HIM UP!

GET IT IN THE MIDDLE, MOUSIE!

GOOD IDEA — IT'LL GIVE HAMISH A CLEAR SHOT AT THE GOAL!

AND...

HIT IT, HAMISH!

SHOW US THE HOT-SHOT!

AYE! I CANNA MISS!

NOT THE HOT-SHOT! LEMME GET OUT THE WAY!

THAT AIN'T NO HOT-SHOT! BOOOOO!

I'VE SAVED IT!

OCH! I KICKED THE GROUND! I SHOULD HAVE SCORED!

MISTER McSPENDER WAS NOT IMPRESSED!

BIG TWIT! HE CAN'T KICK!

HE WANTED TO GO IN FOR THE BIG KICK COMPETITION, TOO!

THE RIVAL FANS ENJOYED THEMSELVES!

OHHH — WHAT A ROTTEN SHOT — WHAT A ROTTEN SHOT...

THEY'RE LAUGHING AT ME! I DINNA BLAME 'EM, EITHER! I SHOULD HAVE PUT THAT ONE IN THE BACK O' THE NET!

PERHAPS I'VE LOST M' POWER... LOST M' HOT-SHOT!

CLEVER COCKNEYS!

Some of the stars from London who have taken their "capital" talent around the country.

Everton's former West Ham striker Tony Cottee.

When Graeme Souness wanted to strengthen his multi-million pound Glasgow Rangers team in 1990 he went south – as usual, some may say. But Souness went to the heart of London's Docklands for a Cockney character who had charmed the Millwall fans.

But in Terry Hurlock, Souness knew he had a winner. Tel Boy was just the sort of no-nonsense midfield battler Souness was looking for to add to his team of Champions.

Hurlock, a Cockney in Glasgow, was made to feel at home by the Rangers supporters who made him a hero just as the Millwall fans had done in London.

Now, the Rangers regulars talk about Hurlock as if he had been born just around the corner instead of hundreds of miles south! His dynamic style is reminiscent of Souness when he was a player . . . an opponent no player looks forward to facing.

Tel Boy was born in Hackney . . . real

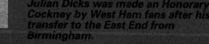

Julian Dicks was made an Honorary Cockney by West Ham fans after his transfer to the East End from Birmingham.

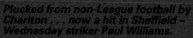

Plucked from non-League football by Charlton . . . now a hit in Sheffield – Wednesday striker Paul Williams.

Paul Ince became a hero with West Ham fans before joining Manchester United in a deal worth £2 million.

Cockney country . . . and was a good honest midfielder in the lower divisions with Reading and Brentford before joining the Lions in 1986/87.

He helped Millwall into the First Division for the first time in their history and won England B honours after a string of brilliant displays against the best midfielders in the League.

Hurlock never dreamed that one day he'd be chasing a Championship medal or a European Cup place . . . but Souness stepped in soon after the start of 1990/91 to take Tel Boy to Glasgow.

Tony Cottee is West Ham born and bred. He was born in Cockneyland and joined the EastEnders from school.

From 1982 until 1988 his goals won over the hearts of the West Ham fans who appreciate good football probably more than any other supporters in the country.

Cottee experienced good times and bad times at Upton Park but the goals always flowed.

A £2.3 million fee took him to Everton in 1988 but while Tony has still managed his share of goals he hasn't quite won over the Goodison Park fans as he did those at Upton Park.

Julian Dicks became an Honorary Cockney after his dazzling displays at left-back earned him the cheers of the Hammers fans.

Dicks began his career with Birmingham but came to West Ham in 1987/88. A penalty expert, Dicks is the typical full back of the Nineties . . . solid in defence and always willing to go forward and supplement his attack.

Billy Bonds made Dicks captain of the Hammers as they sought to regain their First Division status, but it was a pity that Dicks suffered a knee injury in 1990/91 that restricted his appearances.

Paul Ince was born in Ilford, a Fatima Whitbread stone's throw from West Ham, and he

CONTINUED OVERLEAF

Kenny Sansom was born in the heart of South London – Camberwell – and made his name as a dashing full-back for Crystal Palace. He joined Arsenal in a £1 million deal that took Clive Allen to Highbury and went on to become England's established left-back for much of the Eighties.

A move to Newcastle in 1988/89 did not work out happily but Sansom was soon back in London with QPR . . . and putting on some capital displays.

The chirpy Cockneys brighten the soccer scene in London . . . in fact, everywhere . . . even as far away as Glasgow!

became a local hero after bursting on the scene in 1986/87.

In defence or midfield, Ince was outstanding and it cost Manchester United a deal worth £2 million to take the considerable talents of the England Under-21 star to Old Trafford.

Londoner Paul Williams was spotted playing non-League football by Charlton boss Lennie Lawrence and it was quickly obvious that the striker could score at any level.

His speed and goal awareness made him a target for the big money clubs and when Charlton were relegated in 1990, Big Ron Atkinson was happy to pay £600,000 for Williams to be part of his new Sheffield Wednesday team

ABOVE, LEFT . . . Get Carter! Liverpool did and it cost them £750,000 to buy him from Millwall.
ABOVE . . . Another former Millwall star, Terry Hurlock, is a hit with Glasgow Rangers.
RIGHT . . . QPR's experienced left-back Kenny Sansom.

bidding to get back into the top flight.

Jimmy Carter was once given a free transfer by Steve Coppell at Crystal Palace. The winger was given a chance by QPR but did not make the grade.

Millwall took Carter back to South London and it was third time lucky as his speed down the flanks became a feature of the Lions' play.

But everyone was surprised when Liverpool came in for Carter in 1991, paying £750,000 to take the Londoner to Anfield.

MILLION POUND MARVELS

Some of the soccer millionaires who have been bargains ... even at £1 million or more!

It is a sign of the times that when a club pays £1 million for a player these days the fee is not considered particularly high.

After all, Juventus paid Fiorentina a cool £8 million in 1990 to make Italy's World Cup star Roberto Baggio soccer's costliest player.

It was Trevor Francis who first broke the £1 million barrier in England when Brian Clough took him from Birmingham to Nottingham Forest in February 1979.

Since then, there have been countless transfers for that sum or more in Britain. At one time Graeme Souness

Chris Waddle ... a big hit in France with Marseille.

seemed intent on signing a team of millionaires for Glasgow Rangers!

Many millionaires have proved to be a snip even at that price . . . a few have been disappointing.

One club certainly not complaining are Marseille, who paid £4.5 million for Tottenham's Chris Waddle in 1989, the biggest fee ever received by a British club.

Spurs' loss was the French club's gain and Waddle soon had the Marseille fans saying "ooh la la" with his dazzling displays on the wing. A Championship medal in his first season with Marseille was followed by more success but thankfully not all of our top players have gone to play abroad.

One who returned from European duty was Mark Hateley who, after multi-million pound moves to AC Milan and Monaco, came back to British football with Glasgow Rangers.

LEAGUE TEST

Another star who made a similar journey was Anders Limpar, Arsenal's Swedish international forward, who wanted to test himself in the Football League.

His £1.3 million move from Cremonese of Italy surprised a few people but George Graham had done his homework and Limpar soon became a Highbury hero with his tricky ball skills and ability to score goals out of nothing.

Dennis Wise's £1.6 million move from Wimbledon to Chelsea could have been made for about £1 on the Underground!

Wise made the short trip across South West London in 1990 – amazingly he was once given a free transfer by Southampton.

He was joined at Stamford Bridge by another millionaire – Andy Townsend who cost the Blues £1.3 million from Norwich.

Townsend is an all-purpose midfielder in the Bryan Robson mould. He was given the chance to play international football by the Republic of Ireland under the

Across the bottom of the pages (left to right) . . . Mark Hateley (Glasgow Rangers), Anders Limpar (Arsenal), Dennis Wise (Chelsea), Gary McAllister (Leeds) and Gary Pallister (Manchester United) . . . all millionaires and hits with their clubs.

parentage ruling but how Graham Taylor must wish the Maidstone-born star could be in his England set-up.

When Alex Ferguson paid £2.3 million to bring Middlesbrough's Gary Pallister to Manchester United in 1989, the defender became the record transfer between British clubs.

HEIGHT AND STEEL

Pallister has given the United defence height and steel . . . qualities which the Reds showed as they won the FA Cup in 1990.

With Steve Bruce, Pallister forged a partnership in the centre of United's defence which gave opposing forwards a difficult time in every match . . . and Fergie

CONTINUED OVERLEAF

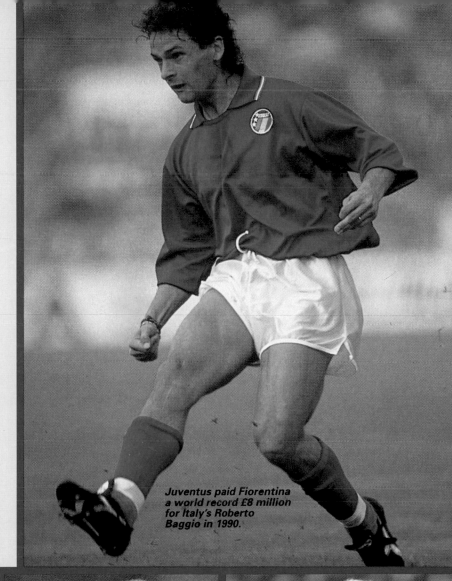

Juventus paid Fiorentina a world record £8 million for Italy's Roberto Baggio in 1990.

LEFT
Handy Andy . . .
Chelsea's Andy
Townsend is an all-
purpose midfielder in
the Bryan Robson
mould.
RIGHT
Mike Newell found
the competition for
places at Everton
fierce after his £1.1
million move from
Leicester.
BELOW
Dalian Atkinson went
to Real Sociedad for
£1.7 million.

may pay £10 million for a player . . . a far cry from the first £100 transfer which took Willie Groves from West Brom to Aston Villa in 1892!

MILLION POUND MARVELS
CONTINUED

reckons Pally is worth at least double what he paid for him now.

Mike Newell began his career with Crewe and after spells with Wigan, Luton and Leicester finally hit the big time with a £1.1 million move to Everton.

The competition for places at Goodison Park is fierce, however, and even a millionaire's tag doesn't guarantee you a regular place in the side

. . . as Newell discovered. Another former Leicester player – Gary McAllister – had better luck with a £1 million move to Leeds. The Scot soon showed that he was not out of place at the highest level and at the end of his first season in Division One – 1990/91 – McAllister, who turned down a move to Nottingham Forest, was recognised as one of the top midfielders in the League.

One day a British club

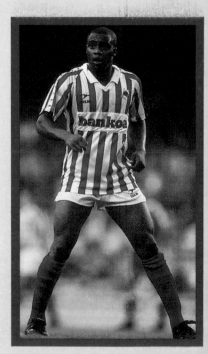

The one man in soccer who can never win is the referee. When he gives a decision to a team, chances are the opponents will disagree . . . no matter how obvious the foul.

The poor old ref comes in for criticism left, right and centre. If he awards a goal-kick, one team thinks it's a corner – when the ball goes out of play both sides will claim the throw-in.

The referee may have few friends, yet within the game most critics accept that British referees are probably the best in the world.

They are always in demand for big European ties and international matches because UEFA and FIFA, soccer's ruling bodies, know that Football League whistlers can be relied upon to control even the most volatile of games.

Yet the job of a referee is both difficult and thankless. When he has a good game, few people will go away thinking "that ref did well today."

One controversial decision and the ref will be as popular as cold school dinners!

The introduction of the slow motion action replay has

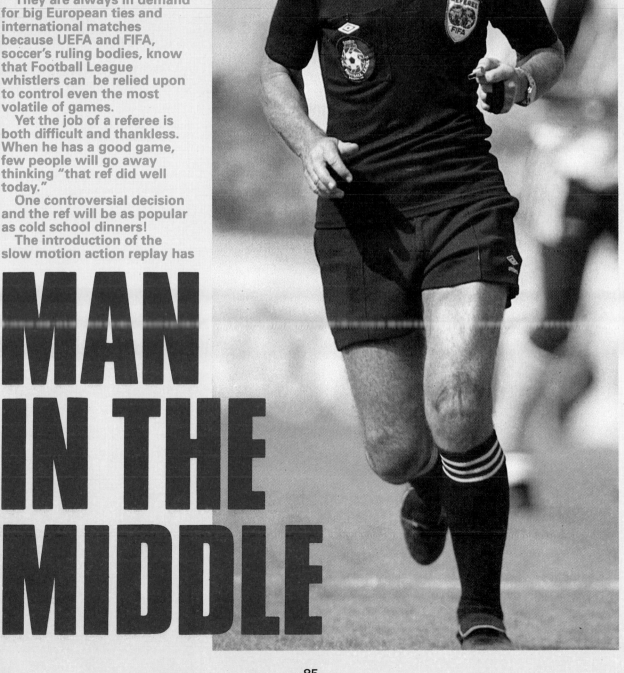

George Courtney, the Spennymoor official, was awarded the MBE for his services to football in 1990.

MAN IN THE MIDDLE

George Courtney took charge of Italy's game against Uruguay in the 1990 World Cup Finals. The game went off smoothly and George's competent refereeing enabled the tie to flow freely. There were few controversial moments even though so much was at stake and the English ref received praise for his handling of the game.

MAN IN THE MIDDLE

put even more pressure on officials.

Many First Division games are televised with goals and highlights shown while most weeks during the season there is at least one live match.

This means that virtually every decision the referee makes – a decision that has to be made on the spot in a split second – can be scrutinised, examined, played back and talked about in the comfort of a TV studio.

Yet most times the ref is proved correct – just as his linesmen are with hairline offside decisions.

Of course, referees make mistakes. Strikers miss goals . . . goalkeepers let the ball slip from their hands . . . defenders miss tackles . . . errors are part and parcel of football.

But by and large referees do a difficult job extremely well under testing circumstances.

There have been calls for full-time professional referees. The referees are already very professional in the way they go about their task, training through the week, writing reports and attending meetings.

Being a League referee is virtually a full-time

occupation and officials are lucky that their bosses at work are understanding about taking time off to control games.

The introduction of the sending-off for the "professional foul" in 1990 made the ref's job even more demanding as they showed the red card to players who stop opponents from having a goalscoring opportunity.

Yet players who foul opponents as they are about to score should be punished. Don't boo the ref if he sends off someone for a last ditch desperate tackle that is against the spirit of football.

People are quick to have a go at refs, yet only when you have tried your hand at refereeing do you realise just what a tough job it is.

And there is far more to being a ref than taking charge of a game. A ref has to be at the ground early to talk to officials from the home club and the police about various arrangements.

When the weather is bad, it is his decision if the game is played. He has to ask himself if an icy pitch would be dangerous to players . . . or whether a rain soaked surface would make the match a farce.

He would have to look at the terraces to decide whether they could be a danger to spectators. If they

are covered in snow people could slip over and hurt themselves.

Before each match, the referee speaks to the managers of both sides, reminding them of little things, such as players retreating 10 yards from a free kick or ensuring that each player wears shinguards that have to be covered by socks.

Once the game starts the referee is in sole charge. No-one, not even his linesmen,

Joe Worrall . . . a firm but fair referee who is respected by players and managers alike.

86

may enter the field of play without his permission . . . and nobody must leave the pitch without the ref's blessing either.

The League are fortunate to have some of the world's best refs.

George Courtney, England's representative at the 1990 World Cup Finals, was awarded the MBE for his services to the game after Italia 90.

Like most referees, he is tough but fair, and the players know where they are with him.

Consistency is paramount.

The experienced Keith Hackett is a favourite of the players – he treats them like men and is always willing to have a laugh at the right moment.

Joe Worrall is another who is firm but fair. Often you'll see Joe run alongside a player with a word of warning if the player has stepped out of line.

Despite what some fans might believe, referees hate cautioning or sending off players. The most satisfying game a ref can have is if his yellow and red cards remain unused in his pocket . . . and after the match no-one talks about his performance.

Being the man in the middle is not easy . . . but unless you've done the job you probably don't realise just how difficult it is!

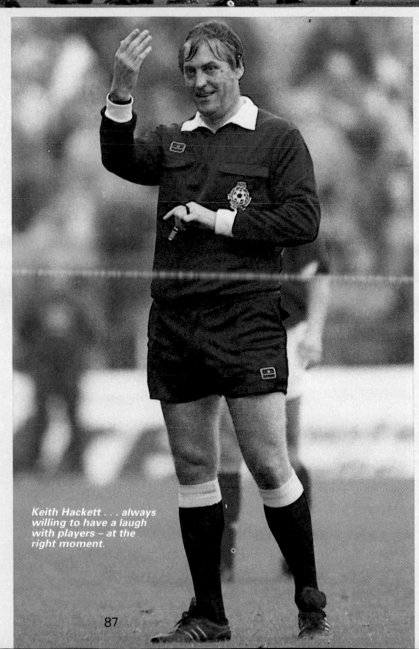

Keith Hackett . . . always willing to have a laugh with players – at the right moment.

ANDY'S NAME WAS BECOMING MORE AND MORE MARKETABLE...

ON SALE NOW! THE GAME

ON SALE NO

THEY HIT THE SHOPS ABOUT A MONTH AGO... AND IN MOST PLACES THEY WERE SNAPPED UP WITHIN A WEEK!

THERE MUST BE A FEW STILL KNOCKING AROUND IN LONDON. I'LL SEE IF MY AGENT CAN GET ME A FEW.

YOU'RE A PAL, ANDY.

NEXT DAY...

HEY! THIS "STOP THE PLAYMAKER!" IS A GOOD GAME, PAUL. IT MAKES YOU THINK.

HAVE YOU ACTUALLY PLAYED AGAINST ANDY STEEL YET?

STOP THE PLAYMAKER

PAUL BRIGHT, SOCCER'S NEWEST YOUNG STAR, PLAYED FOR FIRST DIVISION PACKENHAM HOTSPUR...

NO. HE MOVED FROM MILLSIDE TO LANDS PARK IN DIVISION TWO BEFORE I GOT MY FIRST TEAM SPOT.

THE TIMES

PAUL BRIGHT A SHINING PROSPECT!

LONDON DAILY NEWS

THIS 16-YEAR-OLD IS THE BEST DISCOVERY SINCE ANDY STEEL!

Sun

TEENAGER MAKES SPURS MIDFIELD SLOT HIS OWN!

...4, 5, 6! YES!

NICE ONE, PAUL! YOU'VE STOPPED THE PLAYMAKER!

YOU'RE A NATURAL AT THIS GAME. YOU DO IT EVERY TIME!

THEN WE'D BETTER WAIT AND SEE IF I CAN DO IT IN **REAL LIFE!** LANDS PARK VISIT US IN THE 3RD ROUND OF THE F.A. CUP NEXT MONTH. IT SHOULD BE QUITE A GAME!

THE COACH OF THE NORTH LONDON GIANTS WAS A SHREWD TACTICIAN...

...ANDY STEEL **IS** LANDS PARK UNITED! A FINE MIDFIELD PLAYER. IF WE'RE TO BEAT THEM, HE'S GOT TO BE **TOTALLY** SHUT DOWN SO HE CAN'T DO ANY PLAY-MAKING DAMAGE! AND I KNOW **HOW**...

YOU'RE THE ANSWER, PAUL! I WANT YOU TO SIT RIGHT ON TOP OF ANDY FROM FIRST WHISTLE TO LAST!

ME!

YES, **YOU**, LAD! YOU'RE THE SAME AGE. YOU'VE GOT THE LEGS. I WANT YOU TO FOLLOW HIM EVERYWHERE... STICK CLOSER TO HIM THAN HIS OWN SHADOW!

AND HE'S STICKING LIKE GLUE TO ANDY STEEL! BREATHING DOWN HIS NECK!

SPURS ARE GOING TO TRY AND STOP HIM PLAYING!

HE'S FOLLOWING HIM *ALL OVER*!

THE PLAYMAKER CAN'T SHAKE HIM OFF!

THE CROWD BEGAN TO GET IMPATIENT...

COR...THIS ISN'T MUCH TO WRITE HOME ABOUT!

IT'S LIKE WATCHING TWO TEAMS OF *TEN MEN*! ONE MIDFIELD MAN CANCELS OUT THE OTHER!

YOU'RE STOPPING HIM, PAUL!

YOU DID IT IN THE GAME WE PLAYED, NOW YOU'RE DOING IT IN THE ACTUAL MATCH!

BLOOMIN' CHEEK! THEY'VE BEEN PLAYING MY *BOARD* GAME. THEY'RE COMPARING IT TO A *REAL* GAME!

Ooo

WHEN THE INTERVAL WHISTLE WENT...

BOOOOOOOOO!

RUBBISH!

LET'S SEE SOME FOOTBALL!

IT'S A CUP-TIE! WE WANT SOME EXCITEMENT!

PAUL BRIGHT IS SITTING ON YOU, ANDY...FOLLOWING YOU ALL OVER THE PLACE. SOMEHOW YOU'VE GOT TO SHAKE HIM OFF, OTHERWISE WE'LL *NEVER* SCORE!

DON'T WORRY, BOSS...I'VE GOT A FEW IDEAS!

MY BOARD GAME'S *GOOD*, BUT IT'S *PREDICTABLE*. YOU HAVE TO USE *DICE!* WHAT I NEED TO BEAT PAUL BRIGHT IS *THE UNEXPECTED!*

MINUTES INTO THE SECOND HALF...

LOOK—ANDY STEEL'S RUNNING BACK TOWARDS HIS OWN GOAL-LINE!

WRONG WAY, PLAYMAKER!

LANDS PARK WON'T SCORE LIKE THAT!

SUDDENLY, ANDY SWIVELLED...

HE'S SMACKED IT MILES UPFIELD!